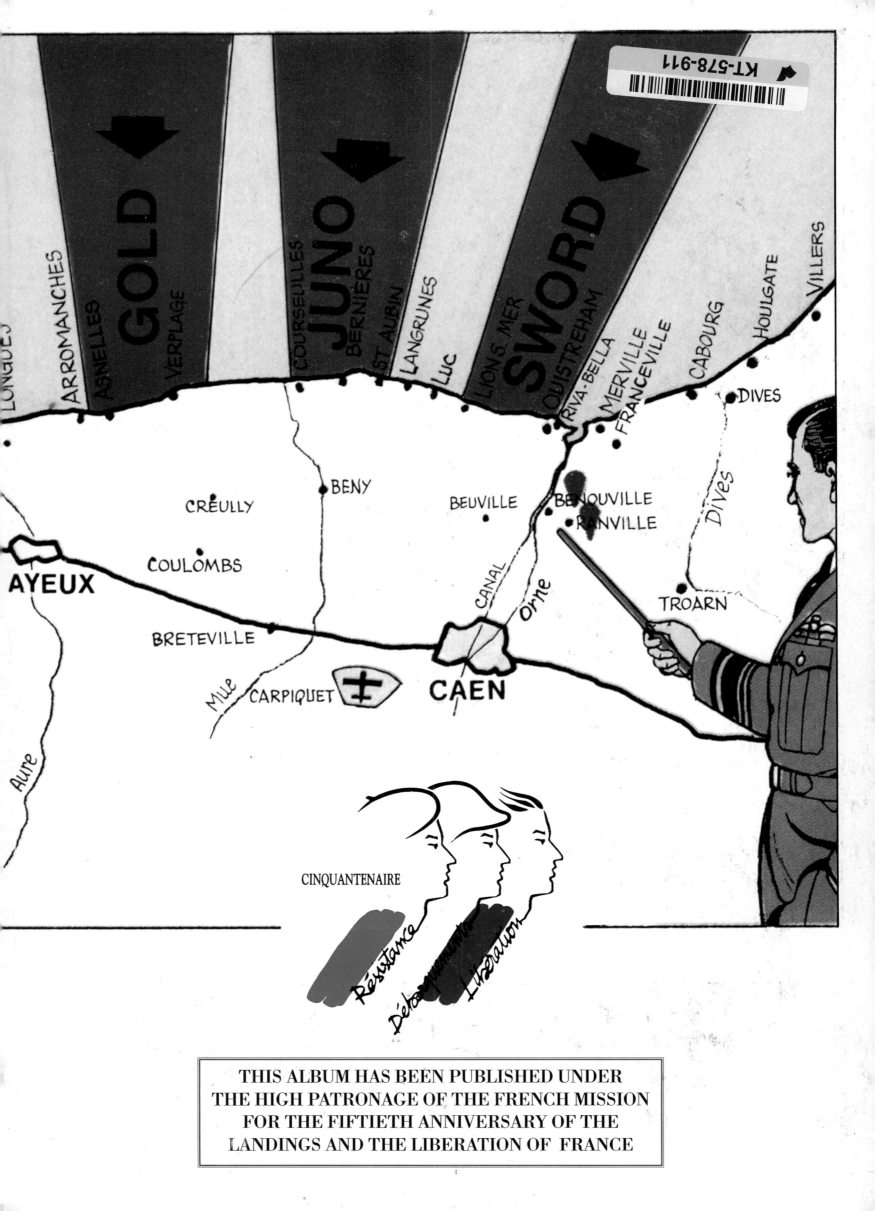

THIS ALBUM HAS BEEN PUBLISHED UNDER
THE HIGH PATRONAGE OF THE FRENCH MISSION
FOR THE FIFTIETH ANNIVERSARY OF THE
LANDINGS AND THE LIBERATION OF FRANCE

OVERLORD
6TH JUNE 1944 - FREEDOM

Script
Serge SAINT-MICHEL

Drawings
MISTER KIT

Colours
Martine BOUTIN

Historical counsellors
Isabelle BOURNIER and Rémy DESQUESNES

Publishers
Antoine CHAMPAIN, Richard GRUMBERG and Patrice le HODEY

MÉMOIRE D'EUROPE

PARIS

In homage
to the women and men,
uniformed and civil,
who gave so much
for freedom.

The Publisher

The authors would like to give their most grateful thanks
to the following people for their invaluable help

Mme I. BOURNIER
M. P .CAPRON
M. M. CHAUVET
M. R. DESQUESNES
M. N. DUMONT
Mme A. GONDRÉE
M. J.M. LEFRANC
M. J. LONGUET
And also The Lyme Regis Library

© MÉMOIRE D'EUROPE / ÉDITIONS DE LA PORTE S.A. 1994
ISBN 2-84150-002-0
Dépot Légal : avril 1994
Printed in April 1994 by Oberthur Press, Rennes.
Registered with the French Ministry of Justice on the date of publication.
Law n°49-956 of July 1949 for publications destined for the young.

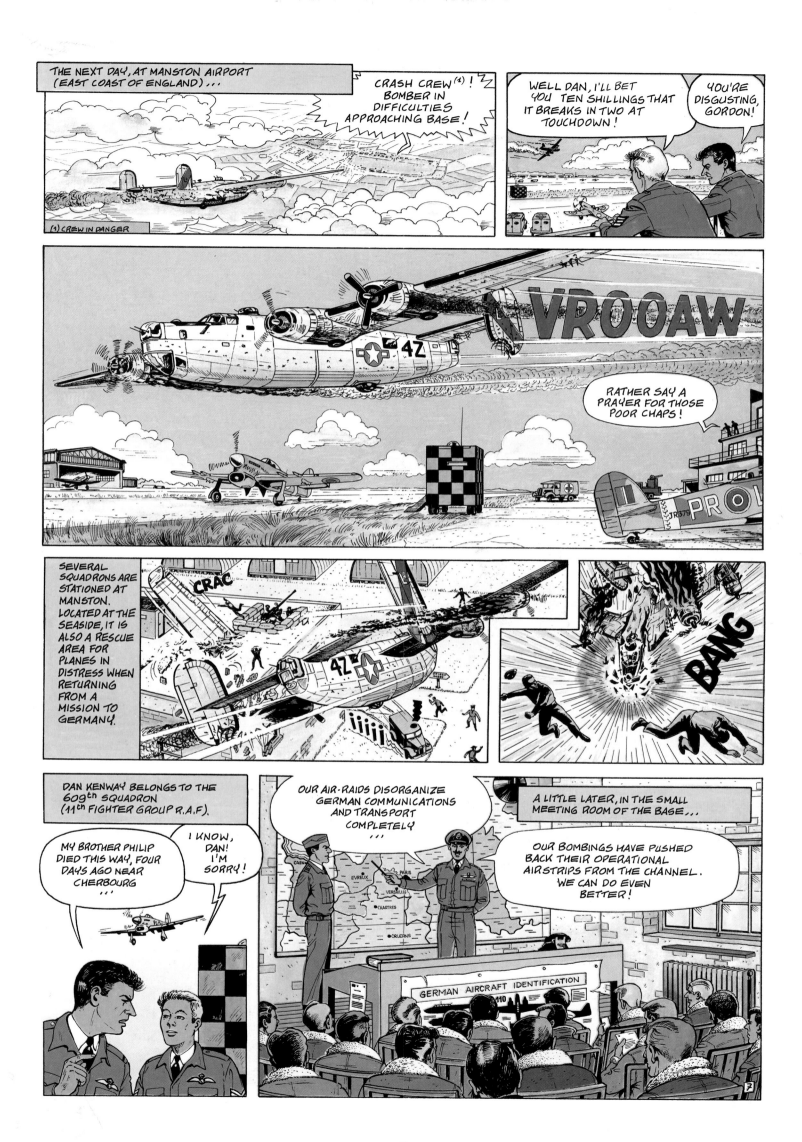

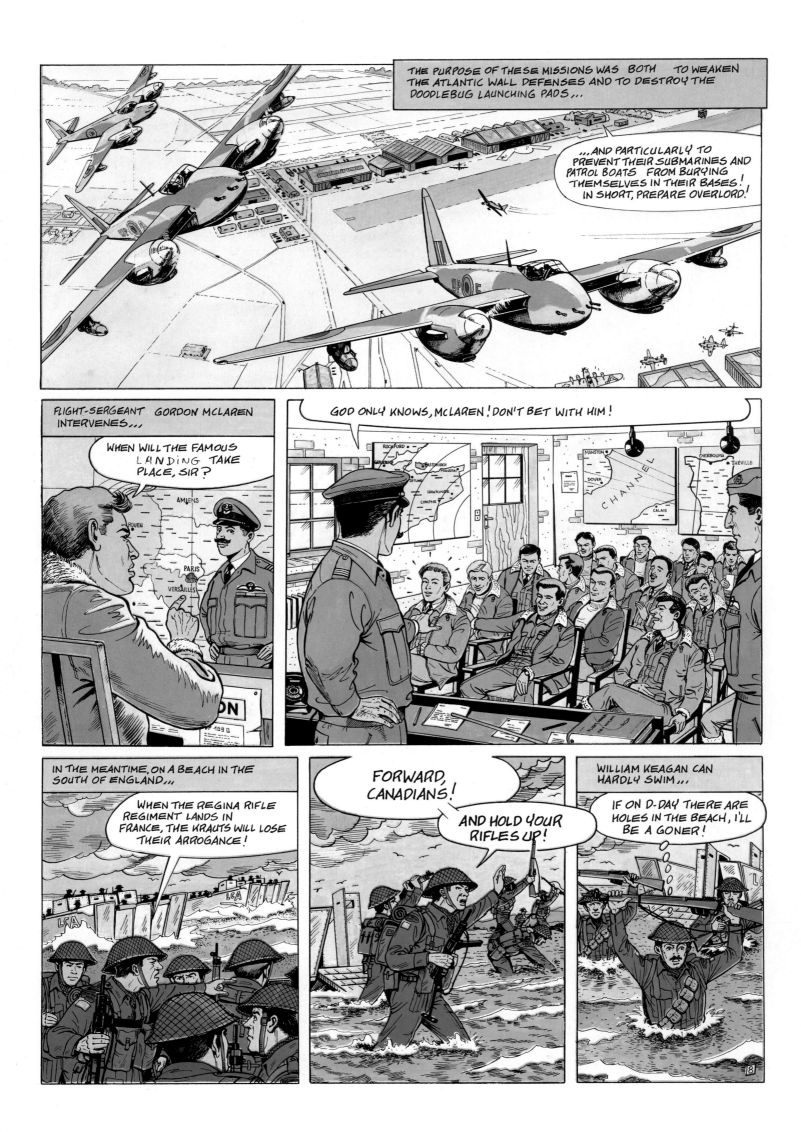

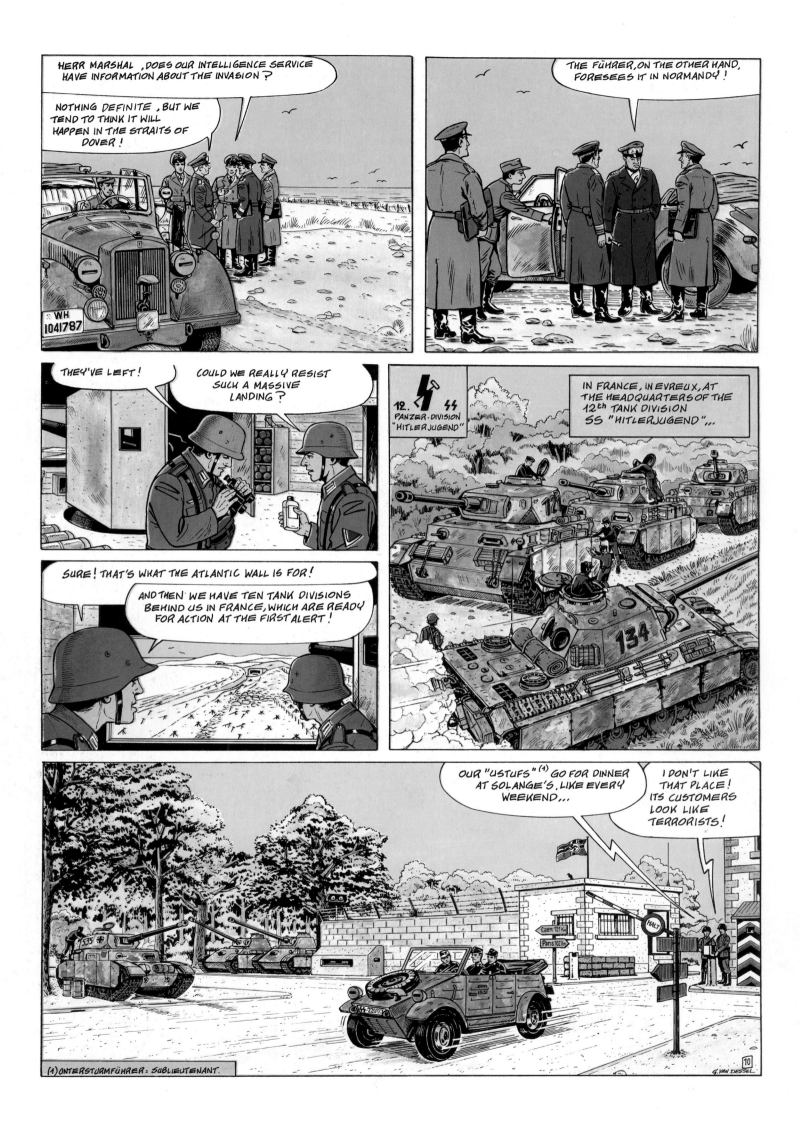

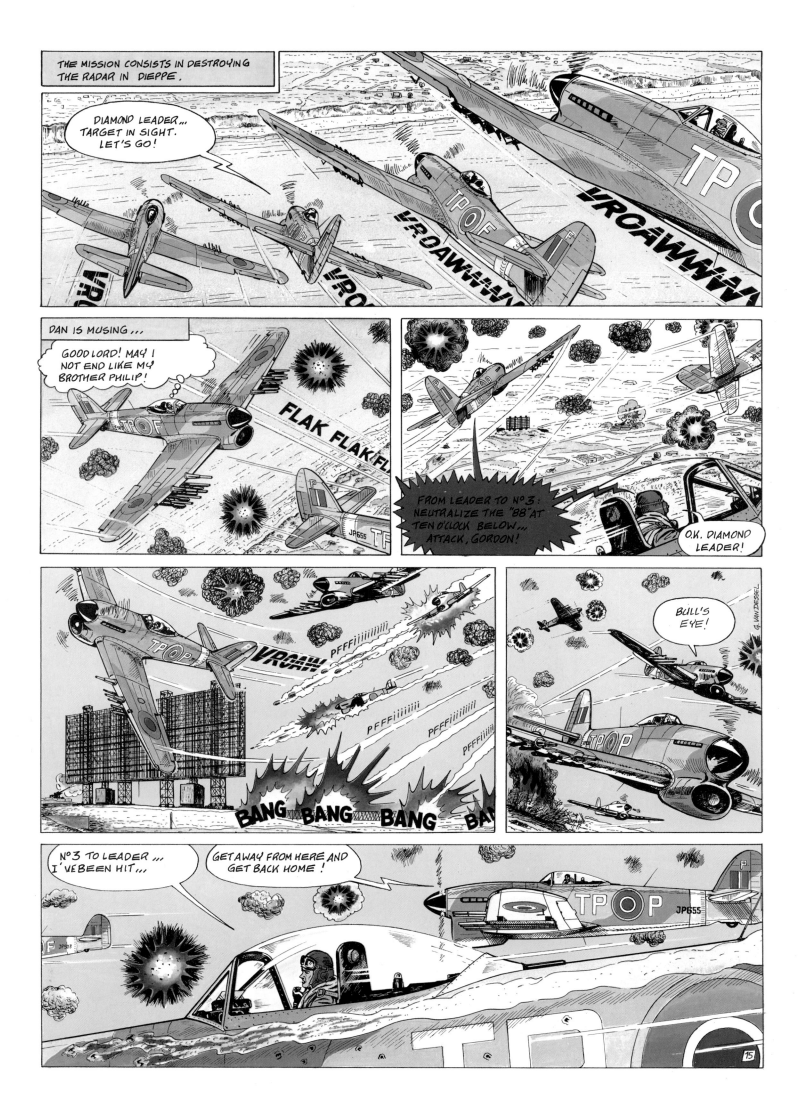

17

ON THE BASE AT THORNEY ISLAND, MONDAY, JUNE 5, AT NIGHTFALL...

CONTROL TO PATROL. REPEAT: YOU ARE CONFINED TO BARRACKS... IT'S FORBIDDEN TO PHONE TO THE OUTSIDE...

WE HAVE ATTACKED THE GERMAN HQ AT ST-LÔ AND BURIED ROMMEL UNDER THE BOMBS!

DAN KENWAY COULD NOT KNOW THAT ROMMEL HAD CANCELLED HIS VISIT TO ST-LÔ BECAUSE OF HIS JOURNEY TO GERMANY...

WHERE ARE YOU GOING TO WITH THIS?

PAINT BLACK AND WHITE STRIPES ON YOUR TYPHOON, SERGEANT! WE APPLY THEM TO ALL PLANES FOR OVERLORD!

WOW! SO ALL THE CONVOYS WE SAW IN THE CHANNEL ARE THOSE OF THE INVASION! THIS TIME IT'S SERIOUS!

THE GIGANTIC INVASION MACHINE HAS COME INTO ACTION. THE AMERICAN PARATROOPERS TAKE OFF IN PLANES AND GLIDERS. IKE HAS A CHAT WITH THE TROOPS...

YOU'LL HAVE TO PAVE THE WAY FOR THE TROOPS WHO WILL LAND ON UTAH AND HOLD OUT TILL RELIEF COMES... I WANT A TOTAL VICTORY! GOOD LUCK, BOYS!

GENERAL MAXWELL TAYLOR IS IN COMMAND OF THE 101ST AMERICAN AIRBORNE DIVISION (THE SCREAMING EAGLES)

WE WILL GO FOR IT, IKE! BUT IT WON'T BE A PIECE OF CAKE!

AIRBORNE

101st AIRBORNE

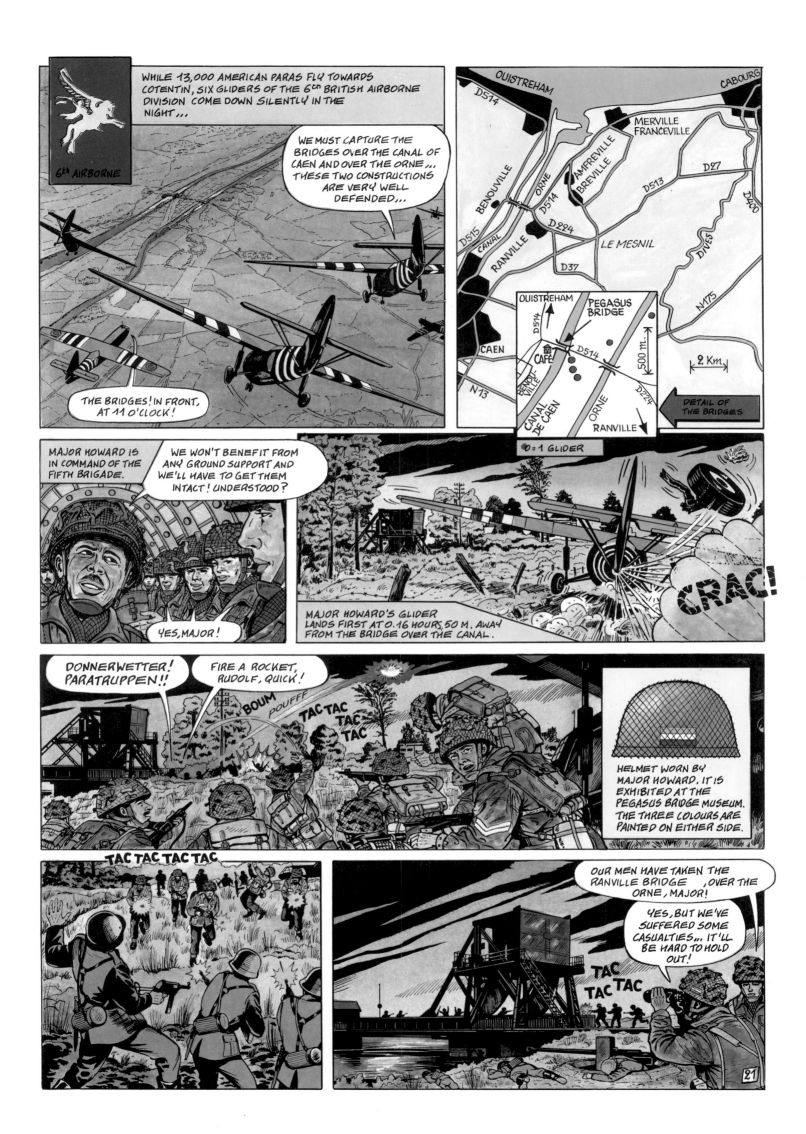

26

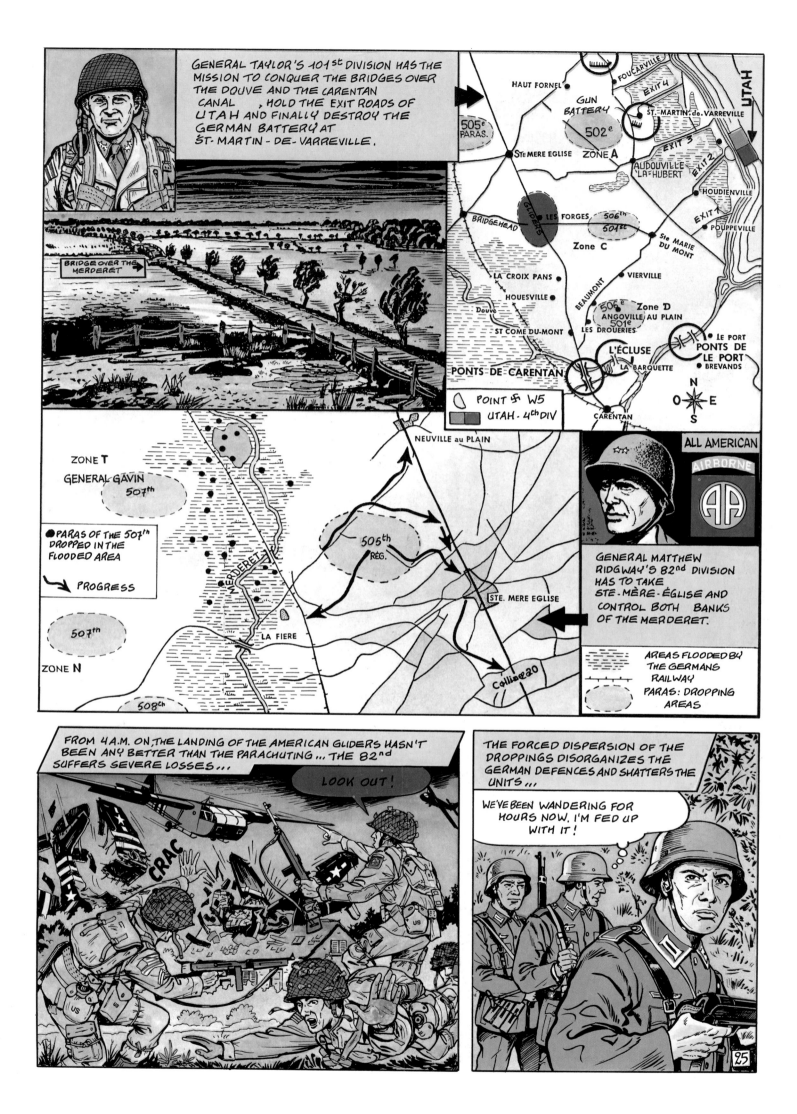

GENERAL TAYLOR'S 101st DIVISION HAS THE MISSION TO CONQUER THE BRIDGES OVER THE DOUVE AND THE CARENTAN CANAL , HOLD THE EXIT ROADS OF UTAH AND FINALLY DESTROY THE GERMAN BATTERY AT ST-MARTIN-DE-VARREVILLE.

BRIDGE OVER THE MERDERET

HAUT FORNEL
FOUCARVILLE
EXIT 4
UTAH
GUN BATTERY
ST-MARTIN-de-VARREVILLE
505e PARAS.
502e
EXIT 3
ZONE A
EXIT 2
Ste MERE EGLISE
AUDOUVILLE LA-HUBERT
HOUDIENVILLE
BRIDGEHEAD
GLIDERS
LES FORGES
506th
501st
EXIT 1
POUPPEVILLE
Zone C
Ste MARIE DU MONT
LA CROIX PANS
VIERVILLE
HOUESVILLE
BEAUMONT
Douve
506e
Zone D
501e
ANGOVILLE au PLAIN
ST COME DU-MONT
LES DROUERIES
Le Port
PONTS DE LE PORT
BREVANDS
L'ÉCLUSE
LA BARQUETTE
N O E S
PONTS DE CARENTAN
CARENTAN

POINT ⚔ W5
UTAH - 4th DIV

ZONE T
GENERAL GAVIN
507th

● PARAS OF THE 507th DROPPED IN THE FLOODED AREA
↘ PROGRESS

507th
ZONE N

NEUVILLE au PLAIN

505th RÉG.

STE. MERE EGLISE

La FIERE

Colline 20

508th

ALL AMERICAN
AIRBORNE
AA

GENERAL MATTHEW RIDGWAY'S 82nd DIVISION HAS TO TAKE STE-MÈRE-ÉGLISE AND CONTROL BOTH BANKS OF THE MERDERET.

AREAS FLOODED BY THE GERMANS
RAILWAY
PARAS: DROPPING AREAS

FROM 4 A.M. ON, THE LANDING OF THE AMERICAN GLIDERS HASN'T BEEN ANY BETTER THAN THE PARACHUTING ... THE 82nd SUFFERS SEVERE LOSSES ...

LOOK OUT!

CRAC

THE FORCED DISPERSION OF THE DROPPINGS DISORGANIZES THE GERMAN DEFENCES AND SHATTERS THE UNITS ...

WE'VE BEEN WANDERING FOR HOURS NOW. I'M FED UP WITH IT!

25

33

47

V2-LAUNCHING BASE, SOTTEVAST (CHANNEL). PLAN OF THE SITE AS IT WOULD HAVE BEEN AT THE END OF THE CONSTRUCTION.

N

180 M.

51 M.

56 M.

PARTS CONSTRUCTED AT THE END OF JUNE 1944.

A SUPER FLYING BOMB?

THEY WERE TALKING ABOUT A GIANT TORPEDO!

WELL, IT WAS HIGH TIME WE ARRIVED!

WHAT DO WE SAY TO THE AMERICAN ULTIMATUM, HERR GENERAL?

NOTHING, FÖRSTER! WE'LL HOLD OUT AS LONG AS POSSIBLE ... TILL DEATH ...

THE GERMANS HAD TRANSFORMED CHERBOURG, ALREADY FORTIFIED IN THE 19th CENTURY, INTO A STRONGHOLD CROSSED WITH TUNNELS AND SUBTERRANEAN BATTERIES. SINCE JUNE 23, GENERAL COLLINS' TROOPS HAVE OCCUPIED THE HEIGHTS THAT DOMINATE THE CITY.

GENERAL KARL VON SCHLIEBEN CONDUCTS THE LAST COMBATS FROM HIS UNDERGROUND HQ IN VILLA MAURICE IN OCTEVILLE.

THE BASES ARE FALLING ONE BY ONE, HERR GENERAL ... THE SURVIVORS PILE UP HERE IN OUR SHELTER ...

AND THE ROULE FORTRESS?

STILL HOLDING OUT ... BUT FOR HOW LONG?

BAM!

I DON'T WANT TO DIE IN THIS HOLE, WILHELM!

CALM DOWN, OLD FELLOW!

59

59

OPERATION "COBRA" STARTS. ITS PURPOSE IS TO MAKE A BREACH IN THE GERMAN FRONT TOWARDS COUTANCES AND TO THE SOUTH.

THE BREAKTHROUGH SUCCEEDS AND ON JULY 28, THE US TANKS ARE AT THE GATES OF COUTANCES ...

DON'T CRY, ARLETTE! WE'VE LEFT THE COMBAT ZONE! FOR US THE WAR IS OVER!

AT THE HQ OF THE 11th CORPS OF GERMAN PARACHUTISTS, NEAR PERCY ...

WHAT ARE YOU DOING HERE?

I'M LT.-COLONEL VON KLUGE, THE FELDMARSCHALL'S SON, GENERAL.

MY FATHER ... ER ... THE FELDMARSCHALL WANTS YOU TO HOLD OUT AND ASKS THAT THE TANKS ...

WHICH TANKS?

THE PANZER LEHR DOESN'T EXIST ANYMORE AND THE FIGHTERS WILL TRANSFORM THE REST OF THE OTHER UNITS INTO SMOKING WRECKS COLONEL!

ALL THESE ORDERS 'VE BEEN CONCEIVED BY PEOPLE WHO HAVEN'T THE FOGGIEST IDEA OF THE SITUATION!

MOREOVER, WE EXPECTED AN ATTACK TOWARD THE EAST AND THE SOUTH-EAST AND THAT DEVIL PATTON PUSHES TOWARD THE SOUTH-WEST, FROM THE OTHER SIDE

HE'LL BE IN AVRANCHES BY THE END OF THE MONTH!

INDEED, ON MONDAY, JULY 31, AVRANCHES IS TAKEN AND PASSED BY. PATTON IS RESTLESS ...

HAVE A BULLDOZER CLEAN THIS UP! NOTHING MUST DELAY OUR ADVANCE!

70

A LITTLE MORE TO THE EAST, ALTHOUGH WITH THE "HITLERJUGEND" HOT ON THEIR TRAIL, THE 1st POLISH TANK DIVISION . (LANDED AT THE END OF JULY) MOVES TOWARDS FALAISE ... IT IS UNDER THE COMMAND OF GENERAL MACZEK ...

LOOK AT THE MAP ... WITH THE CANADIANS WE ARE A DOZEN KILOMETRES AWAY FROM FALAISE ...

IF PATTON'S TANKS PROCEED AT THE PRESENT PACE, THEY'LL TAKE ARGENTAN IN LESS THAN A WEEK ...

POLAND

CHERBOURG

LE HAVRE

CAEN

ST-LÔ

FALAISE

AVRANCHES

MORTAIN

ARGENTAN

FOUGÈRES

ALENÇON

LAVAL

LE MANS

THE FALAISE POCKET

THERE ARE TWENTY ODD KILOMETRES BETWEEN FALAISE AND ARGENTAN ... WE CAN ENCLOSE THE 7th GERMAN ARMY COMPLETELY AND DESTROY IT!

SEVERAL ALLIED GENERALS (AND MORE PARTICULARLY PATTON AND LECLERC) HAVE THE SAME IDEA ... ON SATURDAY AUGUST 12, THE FRENCH 2ème D.B. ENTERS ALENÇON ...

IF WE CONTINUE OUR ADVANCE AT THIS SPEED, WE'LL CLOSE THE DOOR FOR THE GERMANS ...

NEAR FALAISE ...

HEY, LOOK DOWN, DAN ... IF THEY DON'T HURRY TO CLOSE "THE POCKET", THEY WON'T FIND ANYONE THERE ANYMORE!

I DON'T UNDERSTAND WHY THE COMMAND IS SLOWING PATTON'S PROGRESS DOWN!

KENWAY

THE "BATTLE OF FALAISE" ENDS ON TUESDAY MORNING, AUGUST 22. AND THE SAME DAY...

TO ALL UNITS... FINALLY WE HAVE THE ORDERS TO GET GOING TO PARIS...

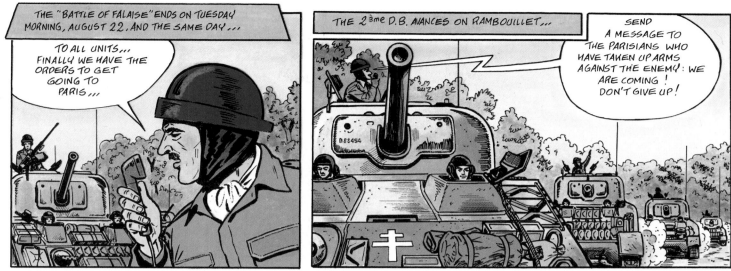

THE 2ᵉᵐᵉ D.B. ADVANCES ON RAMBOUILLET...

SEND A MESSAGE TO THE PARISIANS WHO HAVE TAKEN UP ARMS AGAINST THE ENEMY: WE ARE COMING! DON'T GIVE UP!

FOR THEIR PART THE BELGIAN BRIGADE HAS LIBERATED CABOURG, DEAUVILLE, HONFLEUR... AND GETS READY TO ATTACK LE HAVRE...

COMMANDO 4 TAKES PONT-L'ÉVÊQUE WHICH THE GERMANS HAVE SET ON FIRE...

THERE ARE ENGLISH PRISONERS IN THE BURNING FELDKOMMAN-DATUR! IT'S NEARBY!

YOU'RE ARRIVING JUST IN TIME, BOYS!

WHERE ARE YOU FROM?

FROM OUISTREHAM! IT'S BEEN TEN WEEKS NOW THAT WE'VE BEEN FIGHTING CEASELESSLY AND WITH ALMOST NO SLEEP...

WE WERE ONLY 177 FRENCHMEN TO LAND ... BUT WE DESERVED OUR PLACES!

80

81

SCRIPT: SERGE SAINT-MICHEL • DRAWINGS: MISTER KIT • COLOURS: MARTINE BOUTIN

AFTER THE BATTLE OF NORMANDY

1 9 4 4

SEPTEMBER - liberation of Belgium ; the Americans enter on German territory near Aachen ; fierce battles in Alsace and Lorraine.

OCTOBER - Soviet offensive : the eastern border of Germany is reached ; liberation of Greece ; the Americans recover the Philippine Islands from the Japanese.

NOVEMBER - in France, liberation of Metz, Mulhouse and Strasbourg.

DECEMBER - failure of an impressive German counter-offensive in the Ardennes.

1 9 4 5

JANUARY - irrepressible advance of the Soviet armies in central Europe and in eastern Germany.

FEBRUARY - in France, liberation of Colmar.

MARCH - collapse of the last German defensive lines east of the Rhine, in Bavaria and by the Oder ; American success in Iwo-Jima (Pacific) against the Japanese.

APRIL - in France, liberation of Royan ; the allies conquer northern Italy ; Americans and Russians join near Berlin.

8th MAY - German capitulation.

JUNE - the island of Okinawa is recovered from the Japanese.

JULY - American landing in Indonesia.

AUGUST - American atomic bombs on Hiroshima and Nagasaki.

1st SEPTEMBER - capitulation of Japan ; end of World War II.

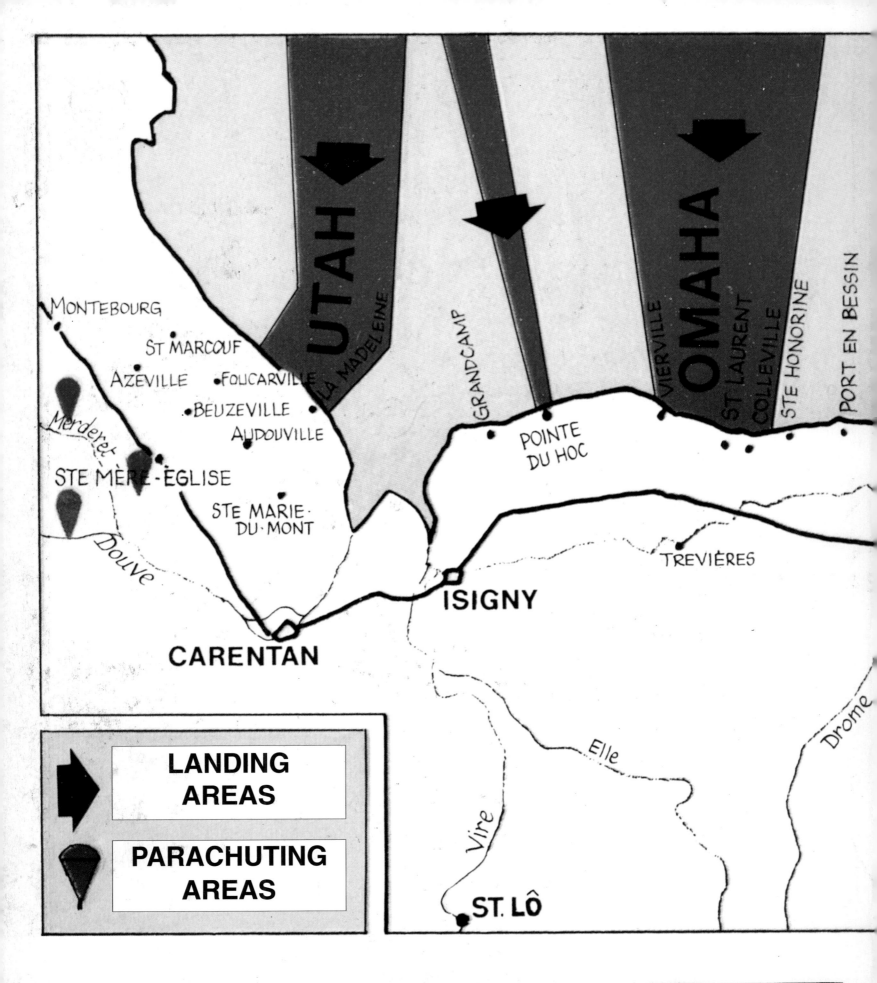

MONTEBOURG

ST MARCOUF

AZEVILLE   FOUCARVILLE

BEUZEVILLE

Merderet   AUDOUVILLE

STE MÈRE-ÉGLISE

STE MARIE DU·MONT

UTAH

LA MADELEINE

GRANDCAMP

POINTE DU HOC

VIERVILLE   OMAHA

ST LAURENT

COLLEVILLE

STE HONORINE

PORT EN BESSIN

Douve

CARENTAN

ISIGNY

TREVIÈRES

Elle

Vire

Drome

ST. LÔ

LANDING AREAS

PARACHUTING AREAS